D1742975

The Blackbird Sings

– VALERIE ANSLOW –

An environmentally friendly book printed and bound in
England by www.printondemand-worldwide.com

Mixed Sources
Product group from well-managed
forests, and other controlled sources
www.fsc.org Cert no. TT-COC-002641
© 1996 Forest Stewardship Council
FSC

PEFC Certified
This product is
from sustainably
managed forests
and controlled
sources
www.pefc.org
PEFC/16-33-615

This book is made entirely of chain-of-custody materials

www.fast-print.net/store.php

THE BLACKBIRD SINGS

A catalogue record for this book is
available from the British Library

ISBN 978-178035-711-3

First published 2013 by
FASTPRINT PUBLISHING
Peterborough, England.

Part 1

When God became one of us.
North meets South in the classroom
The Book
On Culloden Moor
Reflection
The Blackbird sings
Four seasons in one run
Verse 23
A day spent well.
If

Part 2

Hebridean storm
Barra
Across the pond
She stepped onto the sand
Scottish menu
Hebridean curves

*A visit to Ghana, running a race and
preparing for a Christmas sermon,
were times to reflect upon God and our
society's relationship with him.*

When God became one of us,
He lost his majesty, his awesome power.
The heavens, which were his playground,
Expanded to infinity and
The creator became a speck on this spinning
     blue planet,
At the edge of the Universe.

When God became one of us,
We saw ourselves in him
Until
Subtly switched, he was made in our image;
The one we show as we turn to face the mirror,
The perfect 'me', in soft focus and gentle tones.

God, who made the heavens,
Who existed before time itself,
Shrunk to a size we can manage.
Small enough to fit into a pocket, like a first aid
     kit.
Pretty enough to wear, like a fashion accessory.
Smooth to hold; nothing uncomfortable please.

When we became like God,
We looked and saw that our lives were good.
Our small lives at the centre of the Universe.
Look, we said, and marvelled at what we had
    made.
See, we whispered, our strength, our wisdom, is
    all we require.
We are invincible.
What need have we of a God who is a weak,
    puking baby,
Or a man crucified and dead.

When God became one of us
We stripped him of his power,
Stole his throne and stepped into his shoes.
And then when things go wrong,
And we haven't got the answers, ask –
"Where is He?"

VA Nov. 2010

*Following a visit to a school in Sunyani,
Ghana, I reflected on the culture change
in that country as technological
communication transforms
the developing world.*

North meets South in the classroom.
Eager eyed adults ready to learn
About the other half;
Comparing, questioning, wondering.

Traditional and new merge in the mind.
Cultures fuse and combine as doors are opened;
Too wide and all is swept away,
Too narrow and impatience carries off the youth.

The old sit, huddled and tut.
As the young dance to a new tune.

Drumming	Google
Awaaba	Facebook
Barter	Ebay
Chiefs	Questioning
Kenkey	Chips
Old	New
South	North

A Cultural soup.

This poem, written in the 400th year of the King James Bible, was inspired by a visit to Ghana, where Bible verses are displayed on cars and Christians quote the bible in everyday conversations.

A continent carved up and taken,
Its hidden riches plundered.
People chained, sold, abused
Years of imperialist greed, and
In return we gave a book,
A library in a book;
The Word.
"Let us pray" and while eyes were closed,
We took the land.
"Our Father, who is in Heaven......"
We gave them the book, whose word brings life.

And the winds of change blew
And justice rolled on like a stream
And faith there remained firm and grew
As the continent became free.

We gave them the book,
In exchange for riches.
We traded our souls for gold, for food to satisfy
    our bodies
And gradually, like a seeping cess pit,

We replaced the Word with stuff.
Stuff to consume, stuff to wear,
Stuff to drown out the despair, to lessen the
    pain,
And to silence the yearning
That replaced the Word, the book.

VA Feb. 2011

In July 2011 when Britain was at war with Iraq, British gun-ships were off the coast of Libya, and drought and famine were killing thousands in Somalia, I discovered the national monument on Culloden Moor, Scotland where a massacre took place in 1746.

On Culloden Moor

The mist hung over the moor, where
Two hundred years ago the clans dare
To meet the English.
In a battle, awful and fierce,
Culloden with blood was pierced
And thousands lay dead.

Coaches roll up, visitors step out
To explore the site and read about
Red versus blue.
Quietly reflecting their nations past
They pray for peace to last
On these shores.

The sun beat on the desert, where
Parched lips and sunken eyes despair
As death comes.

Daily the battle for life is fought
Against hunger and diseases caught,
Through poverty.

Where is the memorial to mark the time
When millions suffer as we decline
To act decisively.
Will our children look on and cry
When they realize we let them die
Needlessly.

Afghan, Libya, Iraq, we go to war
Justifying our righteous cause
With human rights.
No warships and furtive night-time strikes
Is enough to beat poverty's might
On other shores.

Our heart's not with the poor, whose eyes
Implore us to hear their desperate cries
Of poverty.
We fear being dragged down as we help them up,
So we turn away, raise the victor's cup
'Cos Jack's OK.

Reflection

The alarm and sunlight tip the sleeper
Out into another day.
Bleary eyed, and hair ruffled,
She stumbles down to the kitchen
And – tea.
No one to judge her, no one to impress,
She slouches, mismatched
In old cardi and shirt,
Until the time comes to cover up the featureless
face.
At the mirror, shiny and smooth,
There's colour and shape, a smile and ......
As the reflection and self meet
On the smooth, shiny surface.
Like a long lost friend, she smiles,
Catches her glance and holds it there.
Taking pencil and brush, colour and tint,
She defines the eyes, the lips
Creating a mask, a reflection to wear,
For others to see.
A dim reflection of what is real.
Behind the veil lie....
Anger, cynicism, futility,
The lines of age and regret.
As she applies the finishing touches,

Adopts the smile and the stance.
She acknowledges the truth, and
Prays.

VA. Mar 2012

The Blackbird Sings

Anthony stood at the entrance and gazed out into the deepening darkness. He couldn't see very far, but he was able to sense the moisture that hung in the air at the end of another scorching day. From behind, he could hear the familiar sounds that accompany this time but they brought him no comfort. Instead the sounds added to the weight of the day. A day filled, as it had been ever since he could remember, with tediously heavy work. Along with the other workers, he spent his day building and repairing, and with no completion day expected, the hours dragged with pointless futility.

The dusk of evening always brought on these feelings of melancholy and despair. And with those feelings came thoughts – flooding and overwhelming him.

"What is the point of living when it feels like death?"

"Would anyone notice or care if I just walked out into the night and never came back?

But by the time the moon had risen and the darkness was complete, Anthony's limbs ached for sleep and he had no energy left to consider a new way to live, a way out of complacent slavery. So he turned and scurried into the safety of home.

—

As the sun peeped over the horizon the next day, Tony opened his eyes and felt a flicker of contentment.

By the time he had put his feet to the floor and stood up, the flicker of hope was gone and was replaced with a sense of dread. He stood for a moment wondering whether he could go on with the day or take the easier option and sink back into bed and curl up, foetus position, under the duvet.

But it wasn't that simple. He had commitments and he had work to do; a death to live.

Walking into the bathroom, he showered and shaved, and through these daily rituals prepared himself for the day.

By the time Tony stepped out into the sunshine, his mask was fixed firmly in place and no one could guess what dark thoughts swirled behind it.

—

Waking the next morning as the sun rose above the horizon and the dawn was announced in the birdsong, Anthony followed the other workers down the spiralling tunnels towards the light. No communication was needed because all were encoded to do their particular job. For Anthony this meant cleaning out the debris and taking it to the cliff of red, sun-baked soil, that towered above the ground below. Standing there he heaved and pushed the waste over the edge, and with hardly a look, turned and scurried back into the tunnel.

The sun rose in the sky and Anthony toiled, sudden fleeting thoughts caught him unawares; thoughts of following the debris over the cliff into oblivion. Such thoughts lay just below the surface and would, unprompted, shoot out into his mind, like a lizard shooting out his tongue to snap an unsuspecting dragonfly. These thoughts surprised him, but also came as no surprise to someone who felt life was a dream.

—

Anthony approached the light just as Tony stopped and stood, blocking the sunlight and plunging the tunnel into darkness.

—

Tony stood as though he had seen for the first time the termite hill on the side of the road. Its near vertical sides were red, baked-hard soil, pockmarked with tunnels and crevices. He walked closer and bent down to watch the orderly lines of termites working together to build, strengthen and repair their home.

He looked on enviously at the automatic activity programmed into the termites from birth. He imagined how the life of a creature with no independent thoughts and no feelings apart from sensory ones would be preferable to his own.

Tony stood transfixed by his yearning for a life free from thinking unanswerable questions, release from ambition and expectations; his soulless existence. Even as he realized these thoughts he recognised a new one – that even the life of a termite would be unsatisfying, as termites by their very nature are communal creatures responsible for one another – each as important as the next. Tony acknowledged with some guilt, that what he really yearned for was a life free from responsibility and obligation.

—

Anthony looked out and with his myopic vision saw only that the light was gone, replaced by a blurry face peering down on him. In that moment he believed what others had rumoured, that there was more to be experienced than the daily round of mindless activity. And with that revelation, he tentatively took a step closer to the edge and slowly made his way down the narrow pathway carved in the hillside by the daily dowsing of rain.

—

As Tony peered into the termite hill, overcome with yearnings and guilty thoughts of escape, his eye caught the movement of a lone termite struggling to get a foothold on the red baked earth.

—

In another place, beyond the sight of Tony and beyond the imagination of Anthony, God sat considering his creation. He turned it in his hands with care. He caressed the bumps and smoothed out the hollows. With the care of a master craftsman, he continually moulded the clay into perfection. Then peering through the blue into the deep blue and green, he watched as his latest wonderfully made additions scurried from place to place.

Looking yet closer he saw Tony peering into the crevices of a termite hill. God knew Tony, because he had spent years moulding him, changing him and eventually letting him go, equipped with this own thoughts. And in his centre, God had placed his mark.

And God heard Tony.

—

"What makes us different from the animals, who oblivious to ambition and approval, spend their lives eating, mating, breeding and sleeping? What makes us more than a termite who would not realize if one of their thousands was missing? What makes our lives more meaningful than a spider creating an intricate web only to have it destroyed by a careless movement?

We are born, we grow, we breed, we age and we die. It is a simple as that."

This is the burden that Tony carried and made him stoop down to examine the termite struggling down the dusty path.

—

In that moment of recognition God knew he needed to act, to remind Tony of his deep connection to his maker. It was up to Tony to respond.... or not.

Miniscule in the vastness of space,
Why not let your soul fly, expand to encompass
all;
To see me, who is greater than the human eye
can see,
Filling the universe with light................ yet
Aware of such a tiny thing as you.
Expand your mind and see beyond today.
Behold the infinite in each finite moment
Making it part of the bigger tapestry
That I have woven, and will weave on the canvas
of space.
Look beyond your own boundary.
Take in the view from my perspective as I gaze
down on you.

—

Sydney lay inert in the shadows as the first rays of morning began to warm the still air. His heart beat slow and steady and his eyes flickering as though in a deep dream. Gradually he began to stir and stretch, the warmth seeping through into his subconscious state so that he knew another day had begun. He opened his mouth and tasted the smells on the air. He was satisfied. He did not need to move yet as a meal from the previous day lay heavy in his stomach. He decided to lay where he was and let the sun rise high in the cloudless sky before moving a muscle.

—

On the other side of town, Sid was woken up by the sun that filtered through the gap in the thin curtains. Turning over, he groaned as the excesses of the night heaved in his stomach. He licked his parched lips, moistening them with his tongue that was furred white. But despite the hang-over, he smiled as he remembered the easy way he managed to get drunk without buying a round. His lips curled in satisfied achievement. He had no cares, no worries. He could turn over and go back to sleep until the evening, when he had arranged to meet Tony who, in Sid's eyes, worried too much.

As Sid lay between the sheets, he smirked with the satisfaction of knowing he could do what he wanted, when he wanted. He was content and didn't wonder why and what and if. He thought ignorance was bliss and bliss was believing – "This is it, there is no more, and I have it all."

—

Time passed, the earth turned and the sun rose high in the sky until the shadows became intense, dark circles. All was exposed in the light of the sun. Nothing could hide from its glare.

—

Out of the corner of his eye, Tony detected a movement in the dry grass and turning to look, spotted the long, smooth body of a snake moving effortlessly over the dry earth. The snake oblivious of the sun, yet unable to move,live and breathe without it, slithered through the grass aimlessly. Its tongue flickered and smelled the air.

As with the termite, Tony became absorbed in observing this creature cursed by God, and feared from the beginning of time. He watched as the snake moved over stones and through grasses, its body dry, unlike his own which sweltered in the noon day sun. No family ties for this creature, no obligations, no responsibility, but instead an enviable disregard for his world. A snake eats when it needs to, mates when it is urged to and moves with the heat of the sun. A selfish, satisfied life.

Could I do that? Would I want that? Tony pondered on how life would be easy and not cursed if he chose the path of knowing only the here and now.

The snake crawled on its belly past Tony, moving as though with purpose, but in fact just moving; and Tony, absorbed in thought remembered Sid whom he had arranged to meet for a beer or two.

—

God considered his creation.
Precious to me, you are;
Wonderfully made and
Capable of great things yet choosing the small
ideas
And turning them into time filling actions.
Why do you hide from me in work and pleasure?
Why do you turn your back on my gifts
And refuse the fruit already inside you.
Your ears can hear and your eyes can see
But your heart is a stony seed, dry and withered.
Can you not feel the sun warming you and
The gentle rain softening you?
When the sun is covered by dark clouds,
And the rain beats down as hail,

You still refuse to acknowledge me.
What more can I do?
Meet you in person with miraculous deeds up my
sleeves
And winning words on my lips?
Been there, done that, got the nail marks to prove
it.
My spirit needs to stir you from within.
As a memory of being with me from the
beginning.

—

The evening sun was just above the horizon as Tony stood at the busy street corner waiting for Sid, who in typical fashion was already half an hour late. What had possessed him to come to this place, this post-colonial outpost. All he knew was that life here was just as futile as at home. Poverty and squalor invaded all aspects of life. Corruption spoiled communities. What did he hope to achieve by coming to this God forsaken place?

He was going home tomorrow, but even that filled him with dread.

—

On the other side of town Sid yawned and stretched his long limbs. Moving into the kitchen he picked up a cigarette, half smoked and left by his house-mate. Without a second thought he lit it, and took a deep drag.

He then sauntered along the dusty road towards the corner where Tony stood, shoulders sagging. Sid looked around at the bustling life of his home town where it seemed everyone knew someone he knew.

"Life is good, and God is good," thought Sid as he reached Tony and slapped him on the back. He knew just what Tony needed before returning to the rat race of western living.

"Let's go to this bar I know where this gorgeous singer who will lift your spirits."

—

Ever since she could remember, she had wanted to sing. Music filled her head. Music could transport her back to the days of her childhood, listening to her mother sing as she worked in the fields. Music transported her to a future, full of hope and justice for the oppressed.

But tonight her music would entertain the punters, would make them dance and, she prayed, awaken their souls. She believed her talent was God given and he would use it to make himself known. When she sang in the town centre bar, she seemed to fill those listening with questions needing heavenly answers.

—

And God smiled as he saw Tony being led towards the bar, the only white among so many black skins. He smiled as he saw Tony sit and listen to the woman who sang of slavery and freedom, lust and love, despair and hope.

—

And Sid looked around at the people he knew, old friends, ex-girlfriends and acquaintances, while inside he yearned for something he couldn't name.

And Tony sat and tried not to listen but the song broke into his consciousness and he felt strangely moved by the melody. "I am precious and loved," were the words that kept coming into his head. Through the songs he felt connected to something he couldn't define, but the connection tugged at his heart and made it beat faster. Looking around he watched the faces of those listening, lined faces with the anxiety lifted, young faces softened by a smile, all connected by this one woman who sang of freedom and life. For a moment in that place, God and his creation were one.

Then the moment passed, conversations resumed and life carried on.

But Tony had been touched by his maker, and such a touch, however slight, always leaves a mark.

—

Ebony sat in the comfort of her home, waiting patiently for her partner to return. Patience was her second name. For the last few weeks she had not moved from the home they had made together, not because she was ill or unable to move, but because it was her duty to stay there.

The sun rose above the horizon and with it came the irresistible urge to sing a song of praise and thanksgiving for her life. She breathed in the fresh morning air, untainted with dust and fumes, clean before the heavy sultriness that comes with the heat of the day. She filled her lungs and sang out a melody filled with wonder. She sang not expecting a reply or response, but sang without thought, filled with the same spirit that created her.

—

As the sun peeped over the horizon, Tony opened his eyes, but before the familiar melancholy invaded his thoughts, he became aware of the singing of a blackbird perched on the roof above his window. The glorious sound, a song of praise for the new day, seeped into his soul and stirred again the seed of a feeling begun a few days before and a few thousand miles away. Strangely moved by the song sung to celebrate life, Tony lay there and listened.

—

And God who also listened, smiled at Tony, whom he loved, and knew it was only a matter of time for Tony to acknowledge him.

—

Tony opened his eyes the next morning and listened again to the song of the blackbird. Again his soul stirred ...

Choose a new path and return to me,
For in me you will find contentment
A peace that passes all understanding;
Not the contentment that comes at the end of a life lived well.
Not the peace of mind that comes from financial security.
But the peace that is the unconditional love
From the soul-maker.

—

This morning he felt different.

Months before, Tony had descended into "the pit", and become stuck in the mire of his own thoughts – ruminating in his head. He lost the energy to run and cycle, swim and walk. "The pit" had sapped his enthusiasm. Occasionally he had been lifted up and out, feeling as though he was invincible, full of energy and ideas, but it didn't last and the darkness of "the pit" dragged him down.

What makes us different from the other animals that inhabit this planet? Is it our range of emotions? Our knowledge of right and wrong? A soul? A conscience? An awareness of something which cannot be described, with words that are inadequate?

Tony had all he needed in life, on a material level, but longed for something lost somewhere, sometime since childhood. He longed for innocence, lost when he began to question and doubt; he wanted to be accepted as he was without fear of rejection and failure; he ached to know why life was worth the effort of living.

The blackbird continued its song of praise.

For the first time in many months, Tony got out his running shoes, and began to lace them up adjusting the tongue and getting comfortable.

Stretching and jogging on the spot, he warmed up his stiff joints in readiness for a gentle jog. Opening the door he stepped into the dazzling light of morning and began to run along the road on a familiar route that took him through the park and back through the town centre.

His feet pounded the pavement and his heart pounded in his chest as he got into his stride. He could hear his breathing, heavy and laboured as his limbs continued to warm up. Then his mind wandered back to the singer, all those miles away in a land where hope and faith were a part of life, and love was the stuff that bound people together.

One, two three, four steps; breathing in and out rhythmically as his legs stretched and his arms moved like pistons, forward and back. Tony let his feet move while his mind stayed in Ghana, with Sid, scrounging a drink in the bar and living by his wits. Life is more that filling the time between cradle and grave; is more than being and doing. If that were the case, we are no more than a termite.

Tony felt as though he was running after a thought that was just beyond his grasp. The more he ran, the clearer the thought became, until he could see it, read it, say it, grasp it..........

I need to make choices to follow a path that means the jigsaw of my life fits together as the maker intended, with no missing pieces; yet incomplete as the picture stretches across time and through death into the infinite. Not only that, I need to see my life as part of a much bigger picture where my part is one pixel in a mega pixel film with a director who guides, nudges, suggests and urges. A director who never forces me, like a puppet on a string, to do it his way, or programs me from before birth like an animal acting on instinct, but a director who leaves the choice up to me.

Tony ran on and through the crossroads to the junction where, like a vision, he could look back and view the past as a picture coming into focus, and then look into the future, with its uncertain turns and hidden dangers.

—

The landscape was rough with occasional patches of beautiful, bright yellows reflecting the sun. Tracks led down into deep valleys, so deep the track disappeared into shadows and darkness. And filling in the space between the hills and hollows was a flat expanse of nothing.

He stood looking down, as he had looked down on the termite hill but this time he saw, with the eyes of God. The vision was illuminated by the rays of the sun that pierced the clouds and broke through, spot lighting places people and events.

Tony looked and saw that his life was not to be lived for himself, measured in years and days to be spent like pounds and pence on himself.

Revealed to him were the intricate threads that covered the landscape, connecting places, people and events. The fine threads vibrated with a force that seemed to come from within the threads and from the people they touched. Each thought and action created a new thread or strengthened an existing one and the vibrations could be felt on either end and even along its length.

Standing, transfixed by the vision, Tony looked at his own past and it was then that another sight was revealed to him. He saw a patch of time, empty and devoid of love. In the centre, termite like, he stood, slashing at the threads that crept into his space, his time, his life. Threads that crowded in and threatened to suffocate him. He saw himself swinging his sword, cutting the threads that tied him to responsibility, to love, to demands and eventually he saw himself alone, on an island space, surrounded by a sea of connectedness.

Tony recognised the place and the time and realized that instead of being happy and free, he was alone and waiting for life to begin. He was looking at himself peering into the termite hill, the day before his left Ghana to return home. At that moment of recognition, he saw himself as God saw him, with love, with compassion, with a desire for life in all its fullness. Tony looked and loved himself; and he looked and loved Sid, sitting in the bar waiting for him to arrive; and he listened and he loved the singer whose voice rose like a blackbird's on a roof top in the hazy summer dawn.

Then from the island space, thin threads started to appear and tremble, connecting Tony with the people, place and events in his life. This time he did not brush them aside but gathered them in, and embraced them. He put out his arms to touch the threads and could feel the pain, the disappointments, the joys and the celebrations of those he was connected to. The threads gave him strength and the power to accept all he saw and felt, the courage to be part of the big picture and the knowledge that no one is insignificant or too small.

With this thought Tony's heart beat fast, not from excursion but from excitement and his face broke into a huge grin as he had an irresistible urge to sing, to laugh, to shout for joy.

My soul is lifted up to the heavens, and
My spirit calls out in joy
To the creator of all that is, and has been and will come to be.
My creator, who weaves golden threads
Making a tapestry rich in colour and tradition and culture.
His design is always changing and consistently renewed,
Full of energy and life as the threads weave through dark patches bringing light.
My spirit yearns to be part of the picture,
To know again, what my soul has always known,
To accept with gratitude the threads connecting me to others.
To hear again, as those prophets of old heard,
The voice of the weaver as he brings pattern out of chaos,
And with his hand makes all things possible through the threads he weaves.

—

Tony had stopped running away and had begun to weave his way home.

The Isle of Skye is known as the Misty Isle, where the weather is very changeable as I discovered on an early morning run from the campsite to the shore and back.

Four seasons in one run

Leaving the campers asleep (?) and the
    caravanners smugly snug,
I stretched out onto the road running ahead.
The Quirang, grey covered in a blanket of cloud
Neatly edging the hairpins and peat bogs.

The summer sun pierced the sky and spot
    lighted the white crofts
Serving B & B to hopeful southerners,
Who looked out, anticipating Munroe's and
    eagles.

But hopes were dashed as horizontal autumn
    rain
Splashed moors, drenching all.
Recently shaved sheep, chewing the lush grass,
Moved quickly as I lumbered past to the boulder
    strewn beach.

The winter gales blew the rain, whipping the sea,
Bullying me, tugging me, laughing at my efforts
To beat the elements, to turn back time
And keep alive the mind's eye image of youth.

A warm spring breeze caressed my face,
Blow dried my hair and renewed my strength.
As the sun broke through, I quickened my pace, until
 Reaching the still quiet campsite, my spirit sang out
At the variety, the never-a-dull-moment feeling, of this Misty Isle.

VA Aug 2010

While cycling Coast to Coast, I felt the prevailing wind pushing me from West to East like a hand on my back. It brought to mind Psalm 23 where God is likened to the Good Shepherd.

Verse 23

The Lord is the wind on my back......
Pushing me his way,
The route, straight and the destination, sure.
When the dark clouds gather on the hills ahead,
And the rain falls as tears on my face,
He urges me on with his prevailing hand.
At the Pennine summit the sun breaks through
Revealing glorious moor and valley, farm and field.
When the going is easy, coasting downhill,
Even then I feel him bending the grass.
And if I listen in the silence, I hear him whistling in the trees.
When in my arrogance I see a better way,
He tugs and chides me with him forceful hand.
Where can I go to escape the wind?
Or turn and face him head on – his strength is relentless.
Better to relax and be carried along,

Until this journey is over
And the sea meets the shore.

VA   May 2011

A Day Spent Well

What was all that about – 74 miles cycling from Weatherby to Filey on a June day, dotted with rain, hail, wind and sun?

What was gained by peddling furiously along quiet lanes edged with white keck, scattered with red and yellow, under the changeable sky?

What useful and meaningful task could I have accomplished if I hadn't spent seven hours in the saddle, looking for the skylarks high above, while whiffs of wild garlic were caught by my deep intakes of air on the Howardian Hills?

What could have been better?

VA. June 2013

As I ran the 2013 London Marathon I found the words of If, by Rudyard Kipling, coming into my head and this poem is my take on it. St. Paul likened our lives to a race where we fix our eyes on God and his kingdom.

If you can keep your pace when all about you
Are streaming ahead, pushing and jostling,
If you can trust your legs when others doubt
    you,
If you can wait with the tan toned youngsters,
Or shun the sly smirks and not take it to heart.
If you can run while controlling a bladder,
Dream of a PB or just want to finish.
If you are passed by a fancy dress runner
And are not dismayed or surprised.
If you can fix your eyes on the pace-setter,
If you run, and run with perseverance,
Enduring the pain, hills and dark valleys;
If your feet can pound the rough ground level
And strengthen your weak knees and feeble
    arms.
Then the world is your race track and what is
    more
You will see the kingdom, my friend.

VA April 2013

Part 2

Twenty five years ago they honeymooned on Mull, staying in a white-washed, sea-facing hotel in Tobermory, spying deer, otters, seal and falcons through newly acquired binoculars.

The intervening years saw them returning to Scotland, staying in child-friendly sites with play areas, laundries and local attractions to interest their three diverse off-spring.

Now, they return to the Hebrides, with upgraded caravan, child-less and time-rich, with Bramble, their one year old "bitza" pup. Sailing from Oban across The Minch, they spied dolphins and gannets, and scanned the sea for sharks and whales.

Castlebay harbour, on the small island of Barra, was their first stop on the Long Isle/Western Isles/Outer Hebrides. The site at Borve, clung to the edge of the rocks overlooking the Atlantic, where clouds came racing in on the jet stream and quickly moved on to the mountains of Skye.

Hebridean storm

My God, I had not known your power
Until I was rocked and knocked about by the
    force
Of the Atlantic driven storm,
Passing over the tiny island of Barra,
Sitting on the edge of the world,
Exposed.
Science and faith meet in such places and times.
Did those fishermen cry out in desperation or
    hope
To the carpenter in the boat, asleep and
    untroubled?
Did he, in jest, pose like Poseidon
As the waves calmed and the wind dropped?
The white breakers lash the shore,
While the blue sky breaks the grey, cloud
    stretched across the sky.
Relentlessly the waves roll in and
On the horizon the sky lightens.
And I begin to see clearly
That faith, like the sun,
Breaks through the "Hows" and
Reveals God.

VA
Barra, August. 2012

Barra ain't barren!
profusion of wild flowers
among the lush grass.

White, sandy beaches,
edged by dunes and shallow seas,
haven for wild life.

Glacial scraped mountains
lobster pots and fishing boats.
A summer idyll.

VA
Barra Aug.2012

The islands of Eriskay and South Uist, were shrouded in thin cloud that touched the ground and hid the multitude of lochs and isolated hills. The promised low pressure hung over the Western Isles and turned the islands monochrome – hills, moor, lochs and sky all shades of grey.

A recent survey announced that the people living on the Hebrides are the happiest in GB, which may seem odd to visitors searching in vain for a phone signal and Wi-Fi shot spot. The islanders are happy because they know that although the grey cloud may cover the land and they cannot see far ahead of them, when the sun rises, all will be well.

Over the pond

Eriskay, Uist, Benbecula and Beneray
Home to crofters, sheep and hairy highland
cows.
A thousand lochs linked to the sea
With its harvest of crab, shrimp and mussels.
Cleared off the land, they sailed
Over "the pond" to another land,
Of coves, rocky peninsulas and trees.
A new Scotia emerged, a mirror image of the old.

She stepped out in her sandals and onto the
    sand,
Fine, white, shell dotted sand,
Rippled by the retreating tide,
Leaving clear salt water puddles and
The long stem and fronds of seaweed,
Lying glistening brown on the beach.

Barra
VA Aug. 2012

Scottish Menu

My walking boots have scratched the crusty top
of Stac Pollaidh,
My bare feet have kneaded the wet, doughy sand
of Achnahaird beach,
My freckled tanned skin has tasted the salty
breath of The Minch,
And I have been eaten alive by minute, winged
midges with enormous teeth!

Hebridean curves

The Butt of Lewis is " bootiful"
but the high hills of Harris are the place to be
for me and my mate,
who likes to poddle along single track roads,
while I ramble with Bramble
across peat bog and moor
finding silence, solitude and hills to take my
breath away.
Then it's back to the 'van,
The crofts and the lochs,
The teashops and galleries
On the soft contoured Back of Lewis.

VA Aug 2012